6

Highly Effective Strategies for Making 6 Figures as a Nurse!

By: PRINCESS LOMAX MSN, APRN, FNP-C, WCC

Copyright @ 2019 Princess Lomax

Published by Live Limitless Authors Academy & Publishing Co.

Contact Information
Email: Publishing@sierrarainge.com

Printed in the United States of America

ISBN: 978-1-7340469-1-5

Library of Congress Control Number: 2019916209

Dedication

I'd like to dedicate this book to my forever love Gregory Maurice Burnett Sr. He always inspired me, supported me and pushed me to my highest potential. Thank you baby for being my biggest cheerleader. I will always love you and remember all the good times we shared. Until we meet again, your one and only Princess.

Acknowledgements

Thank you to my Grandfather in Heaven, who instilled in me that I could do and be whatever I put my mind to doing as long as I was willing to put in the hard work it required.

Thank you Sandra Williams for being my forever prayer warrior and holding me down as a daughter that you gave birth to. I love you and appreciate you for always being just a phone call away.

Thank you to my baby sister Borisha Perkins and my sisters through bond for always encouraging me to never quit and keep going Kawana Horton, Devon Williams, Dr. LaTasha Taylor, Timaka Wallace, Aleesha McDowell and Kimberly Johnson.

Table of Contents

Dedication...iii

Acknowledgements...v

Table of Contents...vii

Introduction...1

Strategy #1: Pick a Specialty...7

Strategy #2: Work 12 Hour Shifts..................................29

Strategy #3: Get Certified in More Than One Area......33

Strategy #4: Join Your Organization's Committee.......41

Strategy #5: Become a Traveling Nurse 47

Strategy #6: Earn a Higher Degree 55

Bonus Strategy 75

Get Creative With a Side Job 75

Conclusion...79

About the Author...83

Introduction

Interested in making more money as a nurse? The good news is there are several ways that you can boost your earnings.

In this book, we are going to look at what I believe are the six best techniques you can use to make more.

As a nurse myself, I have unique insight into the nursing profession and into these techniques which I myself have used to advance my career and raise my salary.

Now these certainly aren't get-rich-quick techniques – but if you don't know by now, let me enlighten you:

Get rich quick techniques DON'T WORK!

If you want to get ahead in this world, you have to be willing to put in some work. Because you are in the nursing field, I know that you are not afraid of a little work.

The good news is the techniques I'm going to reveal require differing amounts of effort. I'm sure you can find some things in this book that will help you quickly earn more.

You are going to learn how to break out of "analysis paralysis" mode and start taking specific actions that will allow you to increase your income to six figures.

What is "analysis paralysis"?

Wikipedia, the great information resource, explains Analysis Paralysis (AP) this way:

Analysis paralysis or **paralysis by analysis** is an anti-pattern, the state of over-analyzing (or over-thinking) a situation so that a decision or action is never taken, in effect paralyzing the outcome. A decision can be treated as over-complicated, with too many detailed options, so that a choice is never made, rather than try something and change if a major problem arises. A person might be seeking the optimal or "perfect" solution upfront, and fear making any decision which could lead to erroneous results, when on the way to a better solution.

So what exactly does that mean?
Basically, it means if you suffer from AP that you keep searching and searching for the right/perfect answer to your problem so you will not make the wrong choice or fail or look bad.

AP effects millions of people every day. In fact, through my experiences, **more than 25% of**

the population avoids making decisions because of AP – from small decisions like what to have for dinner to what to do on a Friday night to larger decisions like what house to buy or how to start making more money in your career.

Through my own experience and by helping others, I have discovered the techniques in this book will allow you to boost your income to the levels you desire.

Just read the techniques and choose the one or ones that are best for you. Then get started sending your income upward.

It's as easy as that.

This book is designed to help you:

- Make better decisions and take specific actions that will allow you to achieve the salary you desire

- Plan better so that you are better positioned to make money as a nurse in the future
- Ensure you do all the essential work that makes the difference between earning a higher salary and earning a lower one
- Help you sort through the wide variety of options that are available to you and select the ones that are best for you and your current work situation
- Save you from wasting hours and hours doing headache-inducing research or pursuing techniques that won't work

Here's What This Book WON'T DO:

- Give you a bunch of unrealistic promises about you becoming rich overnight
- Do all the work for you while you sit

>	back and do nothing – in this book
>	you'll learn valuable techniques that
>	you can use to steadily grow your
>	income as a nurse
>
>	• Leave you on your own to figure it all
>	out for yourself

Like I said earlier, the truth is all those "get rich quick" programs that sound too good to be true … really aren't true. **They don't work!**

If you've signed up for one in the past (and most of us have) you know what I'm talking about. They never deliver the results they promise.

The only real way to achieve success is through hard work. You need to take action, success isn't going to just come and find you sitting on the couch.

You have to overcome your AP – which is exactly what this book will help you do.

So let's get started!

Introduction

Strategy #1

Pick a Specialty

Summary:

When you specialize in a certain field,

you become valuable, learn more and will always be in demand!

As health care continues to grow and become more complex, many nurses are making the decision to concentrate their efforts in a particular area of nursing.

This decision can have a number of benefits, including:

- Greater respect and recognition

- Improved job security
- Increased job satisfaction
- More money

Here are 10 Things You Need to Keep in Mind if You are Considering Specializing:

1. Look for an area that aligns with your "personal style."

For example, do you like the fast-paced, think on your feet atmosphere that accompanies working in the emergency department or a trauma center? Or do you prefer work that is more methodical and detail-oriented like clinical research?

You may also want to consider your interests outside of work. Are you interested in fitness and nutrition? Then you might want to look for a specialty opportunity that allows you to incorporate these interests in your work.

2. Look for an area that aligns with your ideal job role.

Do you want to be in a leadership role or do you prefer something that will allow you to work more on your own? Do you want to work closely with patients or would you prefer to avoid direct patient care if you can?

These are the types of questions you need to ask yourself when picking a specialty. You'll really want to get into your own head and decide what really makes you happy.

3. Consider the job setting.

Do you want to work in a hospital ... in a research setting ... in a school? Where you work – and who you work with – can have a significant impact on your level of happiness going forward.

4. Evaluate how well you handle stress **well**.

As a nurse you know that this field can involve pressure situations – particularly when it comes to providing care but also as you move up and advance and accept new responsibilities.

A chief nursing officer or a certified registered nurse anesthetist are going to earn higher salaries but are also going to have to handle more stress as well. In light of this, is advancing something you want? Or would you prefer to have a less stressful position?

5. Determine how important salary is to you.

Since this book is about strategies you can use to make more money, I'm going to assume that a higher salary has some level of importance to you right now. That means you should look for a specialty area that offers a higher than normal salary range. We will talk more about different nursing specialties in a moment. Just remember that higher salaries almost always come with higher demands. You'll have to balance these two things in order to achieve lasting career satisfaction.

6. Decide if you are willing to advance your education.

Many nursing specialties require specific skills, training and/or certifications. If you choose one of these areas, you will need to be willing to spend time to advance your professional education and build your skills. Remember, getting certified is often just the first part of the battle, you may then need to maintain your certification status. So you are going to have to be willing to put in the time. The good news is certified nurses often receive greater recognition, respect and more money than non-certified nurses.

7. Consider where you want to live – and the job market there.

If you dream of living in Miami, then you will want to choose a specialty that is in demand there. If you want to stay where you are, then you will want to choose a specialty that is demand where you are. Study the area you are interested in in-depth and get a feel for what the nursing market is like there.

One more thing to consider: licensing requirements. Don't forget to check this out as licensure requirements can differ by state.

8. How are you with technology?

If you have a natural inclination for technology, you may want to consider a specialty that allows you to incorporate that interest such as nursing informatics or telemetry.

9. Are you a 'people person'?

Extroverted nurses who enjoy meeting and interacting with people should look for specialties that allow them to do that. On the other hand, introverted nurses should look for opportunities that will allow them to work more on their own – such as a nurse researcher, legal nurse consultant, informatics specialist or forensics nurse.

10. Are you willing to advance your education?

Many specialization opportunities will require nurses to have a master's degree – so you are going to have to be willing – and have the time – to continue your education. There are many online programs available now that will allow you to do so while continuing to work. However, you will have to determine if the time commitment fits with your work – and personal – responsibilities.

20 Top Nursing Career Specialties

The nursing field has been growing rapidly the past few years and is expected to continue growing at a fast pace well into the future. In fact, the Bureau of Labor Statistics projects a 15% job growth rate for registered nurses through 2026.

All of this growth has created nursing shortages in some specialties. Here are the current top nursing specialties as identified by the Nurse Journal, along with their comments on that specialty.

1. Neonatal Nurse

These professionals assist patients as they give birth and directly afterward. Some of these nurses work on labor and delivery or postpartum units, and monitor both the mothers and the babies in their care. Other neonatal nurses work in neonatal intensive care units, where newborn babies who are premature or ill can receive continuous care.

How to Become One: Like many nursing specialties, neonatal nurses must first earn a bachelor's degree in nursing and their RN license. These nurses must also earn certifications in neonatal resuscitation, a qualification some employers provide to new hires.

Job Growth Rate: N/A

Salary: $61,212

2. Nurse Midwife

These advanced practice nurses guide patients through pregnancy and delivery, and they are often the primary provider for such clients. Nurse midwife is also one of the most in-demand nursing jobs in the country; the high pay rates reflect this growth, as well as the additional education these professionals receive compared to other registered nurse specialties.

How to Become One: Candidates should earn a BSN and gain at least one year of experience in clinical nursing. They must also earn a master's degree in nurse-midwifery and pass state licensing requirements.

Job Growth Rate: 31%

Salary: $100,590

3. Clinical Nurse

Clinical Nurse Specialists (CNS) is an umbrella term for advanced practice nurses with many different specialties. They sometimes oversee clinical floors to ensure that all nurses use best practices. Unlike other nursing careers at this level, CNS professionals do not need prescription privileges in order to practice.

How to Become One: CNS candidates must first earn a BSN, and then typically practice in their preferred specialties for a few years. These professionals then earn an MSN in those concentrations and obtain their state certifications.

Job Growth Rate: N/A

Salary: $87,138

4. Critical Care Nurse

Critical care nursing is a nursing field that defines itself by the hospital units in which they work. Critical care nurses help patients on critical care floors, which sometimes includes intensive care units and trauma floors. Unlike other nursing specialties, critical care nurses see sharp rises in salary averages throughout their careers.

How to Become One: Critical care nursing candidates must possess valid RN licenses. Some hospitals prefer applicants with BSNs, but nurses with associate degrees can also find work.

Job Growth Rate: N/A

Salary: $66,503

5. Dialysis Nurse

Patients suffering from kidney failure require regular dialysis to clean their blood. This process requires the attention of specialized nurses. Dialysis nurses assess patients before each procedure, ensure safety during the process, and perform assessments when the dialysis is complete. They may work in hospitals or outpatient dialysis centers.

How to Become One: Dialysis nurses need active RN licenses, and can be more competitive on the job market with a BSN. While the minimum educational requirement is usually an associate degree, employers often prefer several years of nursing experience.

Job Growth Rate: N/A

Salary: $66,500

6. Nurse Practitioner

Nurse practitioners are advanced practice nurses with prescription writing privileges who can work in as many different specialties as physicians. They may concentrate on specific demographics, diseases, or departments within a hospital. Some serve as primary care practitioners for children or adults. As the need for medical providers grows, nurse practitioners remain in demand.

How to Become One: After earning their BSN, nurse practitioner candidates must complete master's programs in their chosen specialties. They must also apply for state licensure and prescription writing rights.

Job Growth Rate: 31%

Salary: $103,880

7. Health Policy Nurse

An experienced healthcare worker with a deep understanding of the medical system, these nurses provide insight into how healthcare policy proposals may affect patients. Unlike different nursing specialties, health policy nurses do not treat patients directly. Instead, they work for government organizations and nonprofits to advocate for patients.

How to Become One: Health policy nurses must typically hold a BSN and several years of bedside experience. Some candidates earn master's degrees in public policy or healthcare administration, which make them more competitive on the job market.

Job Growth Rate: N/A

Salary: N/A

8. Informatics Nurse

Informatics nurses work at the intersection of and technology. They leverage their knowledge of human health and experience in bedside nursing to determine how emerging technology can help patients. They advise hospitals, practitioners, and companies that develop new healthcare technology. These positions require excellent technical skills, including those that involve big data and networks.

How to Become One: In addition to an RN license, informatics nurse candidates should have a few years of bedside nursing experience and formal training with healthcare informatics. This training can take the form of a graduate certificate, continuing education credits, or an additional degree.

Job Growth Rate: N/A

Salary: $77,460

9. Nurse Anesthetist

Nurse anesthetists are advanced practice nurses who must hold master's degrees in anesthesiology. They administer topical, regional, and general anesthesia as needed, and enjoy the same prescription rights as physicians. Nurse anesthesiology is one of the highest paying nursing specialties.

How to Become One: These specialized nurses must earn a BSN in general nursing and an MSN in nurse anesthesiology. They must also seek licensing and prescription privileges in their states.

Job Growth Rate: 31%

Salary: $165,120

10. Nurse Educator

Nurse educators use their first-hand experience and knowledge of medicine to train up-and-coming nurses. They work with hospitals and universities to design effective educational programs. Some focus on clinical hours for BSN students, while others teach courses at universities or create continuing education programs for practicing professionals.

How to Become One: Students who want these positions should earn a BSN, gain several years of bedside nursing experience, and earn a master's degree in nurse education.

Job Growth Rate: N/A

Salary: $73,710

11. Nurse Advocate

These nurses communicate between patients and medical teams. They ensure high levels of care and intervene on behalf of patients whenever a problem arises. While all nurses advocate for patients, these specialized professionals exclusively do this work. These nurses typically work in hospitals and outpatient surgery centers.

How to Become One: To become a nurse advocate individuals must earn an RN license, but do not need additional formal education. Applicants often have many years of bedside nursing experience and excel in patient relations.

Job Growth Rate: N/A

Salary: $61,619

12. Nurse Researcher

Nurse researchers conduct studies and analyze data to innovate in healthcare. They can work for hospitals, research laboratories, clinics, or pharmaceutical companies. These nurses typically research topics that may affect nursing — such as ways to make it safer — but they do not carry out bedside nursing tasks.

How to Become One: Nurse researchers must have a BSN and an advanced degree in nursing-related fields. Their master's degree should be research-intensive, and some employers prefer candidates with bedside nursing experience.

Job Growth Rate: N/A

Salary: $81,500

13. Pain Management Nurse

A pain management nurse assists and treats patients suffering from chronic or acute pain. With an estimated 50 million Americans living with some form of chronic pain, this is one of the most in-demand nursing jobs in the country.

How to Become One: Candidates should earn an RN license either at the BSN or associate level. To make their applications more competitive, they should earn certifications through the American Society for Pain Management Nursing.

Job Growth Rate: N/A

Salary: $61,619

14. Psychiatric Nurse

Psychiatric nurses assist patients with mental illnesses. They work in hospitals and in-patient care facilities to ensure that patients take their medications, stay safe from harm, and attend counseling sessions. They can also work with patients who have Alzheimer's or dementia either through in-home care or skilled nursing facilities.

How to Become One: Psychiatric nurses must hold a valid RN license, ideally at the BSN level. Candidates can also earn a master's degree and certification from the Federal Drug Enforcement Administration to become advanced practice nurses in this specialty.

Job Growth Rate: 26%

Salary: $60,239

15. Trauma Nurse

Trauma Nurse

These specialized nurses work on the trauma units in hospitals. Their patients recover from physical traumas, including serious injuries from accidents. Some trauma nurses become advanced practice nurses or nurse practitioners within the specialty. These professionals can prescribe medications and earn more than many of their RN colleagues.

How to Become One: Trauma nurses must earn an RN license and certification from the Society of Trauma Nurses to remain competitive. Advanced practice nurses must earn master's degrees and prescription licenses from their states.

Job Growth Rate: N/A

Salary: $61,866

16. Travel Nurse

Travel Nurse

As the title implies, travel nurses go from one facility to another, depending on the need. They travel between hospitals, clinics, private practices, and outpatient centers to fill staffing needs. These nurses can specialize in a specific type of practice, or be available to work in any role.

How to Become One: Travel nurses can work at any level, from ADN to BSN, but many hospitals prefer BSN candidates. Some travel nursing agencies require applicants to have three or more years of experience.

Job Growth Rate: N/A

Salary: $65,995

17. Pediatric Nurse

Pediatric nurses help children in a variety of settings. They can work anywhere that children receive medical treatment, including pediatric hospitals, pediatric wings in traditional hospitals, and private practices.

How to Become One: Although organizations can hire pediatric nurses at any education level, candidates should earn a BSN to be competitive in the field. Applicants can also earn certifications from organizations such as the American Nurse Credentialing Center.

Job Growth Rate: N/A

Salary: $58,726

18. Geriatric Nurse

As baby boomers age and require more medical attention, geriatric nursing is one of the most in-demand nursing jobs. Geriatric nurses work in hospitals and skilled nursing facilities to care for patients in the golden years of their lives. They are skilled in areas such as memory care and end-of-life nursing.

How to Become One: ADN and LVN degrees often suffice for these positions. However, candidates with a BSN or additional credentials — such as the Gerontological Nursing Certification — tend to earn more than their associate-level peers.

Job Growth Rate: N/A

Salary: $57,500

19. Public Health Nurse

While professionals in most nursing fields care for a few patients per shift, public health nurses look after whole communities. These professionals are employed by government agencies and hospitals to design and implement health campaigns that impact the surrounding areas or specific populations. Some public health nurses earn master's degrees and work in management-level positions.

How to Become One: Public health nurses must earn an RN license, preferably with a BSN. The National Board of Public Health Examiners offers a certification that can make candidates competitive.

Job Growth Rate: N/A

Salary: $57,167

20. Oncology Nurse

Oncology nurses work exclusively with patients who receive cancer treatments. These professionals assist with in-patient care for those who stay in hospitals or outpatient treatments, such as chemotherapy. They tend to work for hospitals, but can also find employment at private oncology practices. In addition to medication administration, oncology nurses educate patients about their illnesses.

How to Become One: Oncology nurses must earn an RN license in their state either with a BSN or associate degree. They can also earn certifications from qualified organizations, such as the Oncology Nursing Certification Corporation.

Job Growth Rate: 19%

Salary: $68,160

Strategy #2

Work 12 Hour Shifts

Summary:
When you work 12-hour shifts, you're only obligated to work 3 days so you pick up extra shifts and the fourth and fifth 12-hour shifts will be overtime. Depending on your employer you will get either time and a half or double time – that my friend can make your biweekly paycheck double the original amount!

Twelve hour shifts have become normal operating procedure at many hospitals across the country and there are a lot of nurses who love them.

Advantages of 12-hour shifts include:

- **A much shorter work week** – with 12-hour shifts a nurse can work three days and have four days off. This can be especially appealing if you a long commute to work or if you have children to take care of at home.

- **Better work-life balance** – With the shorter work week comes a greater work life balance. With this schedule a nurse will have four whole days away from her job to devote to greater enjoyment of her personal life and spending more time with family.

- **Flexibility** – You may also be able to bunch shifts together to enjoy even longer chunks of time off. That could mean more time to spend with family or pursuing a hobby or a nurse could even pursue a second job.

But this book is about making more money and by working 12-hour shifts you open yourself to being able to work more hours and earn more income.

Three 12-hour shifts, followed by a day off and then another one or two 12-hour shifts could allow you to rack up some very nice overtime pay.

If you are able to keep up a schedule like that or something similar you can quickly grow your income.

Just be sure to work into your schedule some time to rest and recuperate.

Working 12-hour shifts is not easy and can zap your energy if you are not careful.

Here are some tips that can make these longer shifts easier:

- Be sure to get plenty of sleep before work

- Be sure to eat a healthy, well balanced diet

- Start regularly performing deep breathing to relax

- Be sure to take your breaks!

- If your workload allows it, take a walk away from your unit to clear your mind and rejuvenate your soul

- Be sure to eat healthy snacks – stay away from the junk food!

Strategy #3

Get Certified in
More Than One Area

Summary:
Having additional certifications will
allow you to expand yourself in a
plethora of departments.

To put it simply, certifications set nurses
apart and open the door to higher earnings.

According to a **2018 Nurse.com report,**
"40% of American nurses are certified." If
you join that number – and especially if you join
that multiple times (get multiple certifications)

you will greatly increase your chances of earning a higher salary.

Nurse.com reported in its 2017 Salary Survey that certified nurses' base salaries are higher than the base salaries on non-certified nurses.

In addition to higher salaries, certified nurses also:

- **Receive greater respect and recognition.** The more credentials you have behind your name the more colleagues, patients, managers and administrators associate you with a high level of knowledge and experience.

- **Are more marketable and hirable.** One recent study found that almost 90% of nurse managers would hire a certified nurse over a non-certified nurse, if everything else was equal.

- **Have more power.** Studies show certified nurses score higher in quantitative measures of professional governance, meaning they have more control over their practice and influence over the resources within it.

- **Are presented with more professional opportunities.** They are not just more likely to be promoted within their organization but they are also more frequently invited to sit on policy-making boards and committees.

- **Are more confident.** A study conducted by the American Board of Nursing Specialties showed that 90% of certified nurses felt more confident performing their clinical duties. By the way, that same study showed that 100% of the nurses surveyed felt personal satisfaction over earning their certification.

- ***Also, remember earlier when we discussed specialties?*** Well, getting certified in a specialty signals to managers that you are a cut above those who are not certified. You are truly "special."

In other words, one of the best ways to ramp up your nursing career is to get those extra letters behind your name.

But what certifications are the best ones to earn if you want to make more money and increase your employment opportunities?

According to Nurse Journal, these are the five best certifications to obtain:

1. AIDS Certified Registered Nurse (ACRN)

Registered nurses with a minimum of two years of clinical experience working in HIV/AIDS nursing can apply for the HIV/AIDS certified registered nurse certification. Applicants must apply for the certification exam and submit payment. The HIV/AIDS Nursing Certification Board must then approve the application. After the approval, nurses can schedule an exam date through Iso-Quality Testing. This computer-based exam consists of 250 multiple-choice questions covering ethical and legal issues, epidemiology and prevention, pathophysiology, and psychosocial issues.

Once nurses pass the exam, they may use the ACRN designation after their signature. Nurses must retake the test every four years.

Cost of Exam: $260 for ANAC members; $400 for non-members

Salary Potential: $91,000 per year

2. Certified Pediatric Nurse (CPN)

To earn a certified pediatric nurse credential, applicants must hold an associate, bachelor's, or master's degree. Nurses also need 1,800 pediatric clinical hours completed within the last two years or 3,000 hours of pediatric experience in the past five years. Of those 3,000 hours of experience, nurses need to show that they completed 1,000 hours within the past two years.

The Pediatric Nursing Certification Board must approve nurses' applications before they can take the three-hour exam, which includes 175 multiple choice questions and a customized introductory session.

Cost of Exam: $295, including a $100 non-refundable registration fee; Society of Pediatric Nurses may receive a $45 discount on the exam.

Salary Potential: $72,000 per year

3. Oncology Certified Nurse (OCN)

Nurses can apply to take the three-hour, 165-multiple choice oncology certified nurse certification exam to validate their skills and knowledge in the field of oncology.

Nurses must prove their competency in oncology to apply to take the test. Applicants need to show proof two years of work experience within the last four years. Candidates also need 2,000 hours of specialty practice and 10 contact hours of continuing nursing education in oncology. The test includes questions on care continuum, oncology nursing practice, treatment modalities, and symptom management and palliative care.

A practice test and test content outline help prepare nurses for the test. Certification lasts four years.

Cost of Exam: $225-$315

Salary Potential: $80,000 a year

4. Family Nurse Practitioner (FNP-BC)

The family nurse practitioner certification, offered through the National Commission for Certifying Agencies and Accreditation Board for Specialty Nursing Certification, demonstrates a nurse's competency in diagnosing illness, evaluating patient needs, and administering care.

Applicants with a master's, postgraduate, or doctoral degree in nursing from an accredited college and 500 faculty-supervised clinical hours can apply for this certification. Nurses must meet the eligibility requirements before they can take the test. The certification lasts for five years, as long as nurses meet renewal requirements and maintain their license to practice.

The test, which can require 3.5 hours to finish, includes 25 pretest questions and 175 scored questions.

Cost of Exam: $290-$395

Salary Potential: $91,613 a year

5. Certified Registered Nurse Anesthetist (CRNA)

The certified registered nurse anesthetist credential allows nurses to administer anesthesia for surgery. Each state possesses different requirements for the CRNA, a certification administered by the National Board of Certification and Recertification for Nurse Anesthetists.

Nurses must first earn a master's degree or higher from a nurse anesthesia program which has been accredited by the Council on Accreditation before they can take the certification exam. The exam requires nurses to answer 100-170 questions on basic principles of anesthesia, basic sciences, equipment, and advanced principles of anesthesia.

To qualify for the test, nurses must hold a valid registered nurse license. They also need one year of experience working in critical care. After nurses meet these requirements, they can then apply for the advanced practice registered nurse certification.

Cost of Exam: $995

Salary Potential: $150,000

One more important thing to remember: Many organizations pay for certification preparation exams and test fees, and they reward nurses with hourly certification differential pay!

In other words, if you want to make more money it's time to get those certifications!

Strategy #4

Join Your
Organization's Committee

Summary:
Being part of the committee will put you
in rooms with upper management
and leadership, which will give you
insight into what the organization's
goals are and what is needed to take
them to the next level.

Nurses are often so busy in their jobs that they are not as up-to-date on what is happening at their organization as they could be.

The value of keeping up-to-date is that you are more aware of not only what is happening in the organization but what the plans are for the future and what is needed now and is going to be needed moving forward.

These last two items are very important because the nurse can use that information to make herself more valuable to the organization as well as to advance her career and increase her earning potential.

For example, if you know in advance that an organization is going to be putting a lot of money into improving its oncology department and then marketing that department to the surrounding community she or he can pursue an oncology certification (OCN) so that they can work in the revamped department, presumably for a much higher salary.

Joining a professional nursing organization is another way that nurses can keep

themselves prepared to move forward in the careers and earn a higher salary.

For example, the American Nurses Association has been in existence since 1896 and represents 3.6 million registered nurses.

But not every RN is automatically a member. By being a member of this organization you can increase your chances of being heard, you can get opportunities to network with leaders in the field and you can also help in promoting the nursing industry to the public, which will increase your exposure and may get you noticed more by officials in your organization.

Here are three more reasons why a nurse should strongly consider getting involved in a professional nursing organization:

Professional excellence –
One of the best ways to get promoted and increase your salary is still to excel at your job. You'll increase your chances of performing well

by staying on top of trends and a membership in a professional organization can help you do that.

For example, many specialties, such as nurse anesthetist and critical care nursing, have their own organizations which will keep you up to date on the very latest news and advancements in that field.

Networking Opportunities –

Joining a professional organization will give you access to nurses beyond your floor or unit. This additional exposure can help you find higher-paying positions and help you take advantage of continuing education opportunities that you wouldn't have known about. This continuing education can then help you quality for higher-paying positions.

Career Development –

With the health care industry growing rapidly, there are many opportunities for career – and salary – advancement that are being created. A good professional organization can help make you aware of these opportunities and provide you with the information and networking opportunities to take advantage of them.

A great thing about nursing organizations is that they are run by nurses and are designed for nurses.

That means they are often the best way to find career growth opportunities and to stay up to date. Remember, if you have a specialty or are thinking about taking up a specialty there is most likely an organization to support you. For example, the diabetic, pediatric and geriatric specialties all have helpful organizations.

There also may be beneficial organizations you can join if you belong to a specific demographic – such as minority nurses or male nurses.

These specialized organizations can help you feel empowered and make you aware of opportunities that exist for you to advance your career.

One last thing to keep in mind: some employers will even reimburse you for your membership fees to a professional organization. That's because they understand the benefits that these organizations can offer you.

Strategy #5

Become a Traveling Nurse

Summary:
Traveling allows you to become licensed in multiple states and could allow you to quickly increase your income by as much as 3X! Plus, most of the money you make will stay in the bank because you also will receive housing, car and food allowances while on the road.

Traveling is becoming more and more popular among nurses as they learn of the many benefits associated with it.

For example, traveling offers:

- A chance to explore new places

- A chance to experience diverse practice environments

- A chance to make new friends

- A chance to receive great benefits

- A chance to receive free housing

- **And a chance to greatly increase your income!**

Here's what you need to know about traveling:

There are currently travel opportunities in all 50 states. Each traveling assignment can last for 13 weeks or longer, depending on the needs of the facility.

Nurses are also able to choose their assignments meaning you can put as much weight on each of the following criteria as you want:

- Compensation package (benefits, housing)

- Professional opportunities

- Financial incentives

- Proximity to family and friends

- Getting familiar with a location you are considering moving to

- Leisure activities

- Climate

Now here are some reasons why you may want to consider becoming a traveling nurse:

- **Higher pay** – this is one of the biggest reasons for becoming a traveling nurse. Plus, the majority of your travel salary may be tax-free because you're traveling more than 50 miles from home!

- **Additional benefits** – as a traveling nurse you may also be eligible for bonuses and free or deeply discounted housing. You could also have travel expenses reimbursed from contract to contract

- **Even greater work flexibility** – you can work as frequently or infrequently as you want

- **Greater exposure to different places and cultures**

We'll talk more about the benefits of traveling in a moment, but first let's talk a little more about the opportunity itself.

As I said there are travel opportunities in all 50 states but the states with the highest number of travel nurse assignment requests are Hawaii and California.

That means if you want to become a travel nurse in one of these states your wait time for an assignment may be longer.

One way to shorten the wait is to be flexible about where you are willing to go – desirable locations have much longer waits. For example, you may want to consider a suburban hospital compared to a larger inner-city hospital if you are seeking an assignment in Los Angeles.

If you are wondering about the job security of being a traveling nurse – you'll probably be excited to hear that it actually offers terrific job security.

If you are flexible and willing to travel, there are always assignments waiting across the

US. You won't find yourself without work opportunities.

Now let's go back and take a closer look at the many benefits associated with being a traveling nurse.

One of the biggest benefits, besides the higher pay you will receive, is a lower cost of living.

Most places are so in need of traveling nurses that they offer lucrative benefit packages to attract them. This means many companies provide free housing. Many companies also cover the costs of utilities and furniture.

As you can imagine, this is a great way to make money fast.

Becoming a traveling nurse is also a great way to pursue other interests – like a love of the outdoors or a love of the ocean. You can consider positions that will put you close to what you want to do in your free time.

Another great thing about traveling is that after your travel contract is complete you have the choice to go immediately into another contract, which if you are seeking to maximize your earnings is a great thing to do.

But you could also take some time off – if you want to avoid burnout. You have total control over when and where you work!

When it comes down to it, becoming a traveling nurse is a terrific way to make more money while also enjoying greater professional growth.

By working at different facilities, you will broaden your skill set and learn new techniques. These things will make you highly desirable to organizations when you decide to settle down.

You'll also be able to avoid "workplace politics." You'll be able to focus on just doing your job and on patient care without worrying about what organization leaders are doing ... or not doing.

And if you go into a practice environment that is not to your liking, a new assignment will be just weeks away!

One last thing about being a traveling nurse: it's a great way to find your ideal place to settle down.

If there are certain areas that you think you would like to live this will give you the chance to "test the waters" and see before making a big commitment.

You can compare different cities and be sure that you find the one where you are going to be able to live happily ever after.

Become a Traveling Nurse

Strategy #6

Earn a Higher Degree

Summary:
The more degrees you receive, the more money you can make. Most institutions have a minimal pay scale for mastered prep rate nurses set at $100,000. This pay scale increases with work experience, certifications, specialties and how well you

negotiate your salary. Never be afraid to ask for what you know you're worth!

As the health care field grows rapidly, nurses are discovering that advancing their education is a great way to gain a competitive edge and obtain higher-paying positions.

In fact, experts say that the need for nurse's with bachelor's degrees or higher is increasing.

In fact, one recent study found a link between nurse education and patient outcomes. The study found hospitals that hired more BSN-prepared nurses between 1999 and 2006 experienced lower patient mortality rates than other hospitals.

As a result of this and similar academic research, the Institute of Medicine introduced new guidelines in 2010 for the nursing profession in the report "The Future of Nursing: Leading Change, Advancing Health." The IOM's target goal is for 80% of nurses to have a bachelor's degree by the year 2020.

Because of the research and the growing trend toward hiring more BSN nurses, experts say nurses who do not have a bachelor's degree should strongly consider enrolling in an RN-to-BSN program.

Beyond that, experts also suggest that nurses who plan to pursue a leadership role should strive to earn a master's degree.

As someone who has earned her master's and is currently seeking her doctorate, I can't stress the importance of advancing your education enough. It is a great way to get a better paying job with more responsibilities.

Here are 10 reasons to earn your MSN (Masters in Nursing) that I can think of off the top of my head:

1. Higher Salary

MSN holders earn much more than other types of degree holders. For example, they earn an average of $12,000+ over those with a bachelor's degree.

2. Higher Career Earning Potential

Over time, MSN holders see their salaries exceed six figures. For example, nurse practitioners with over 10 years of experience earn an average of $101,000 per year.

3. Higher Respect

Earning an MSN has been shown to receive respect from work colleagues as well as friends, family members and loved ones.

5. More Job Opportunities

Master's degree holders will have the most job opportunities in nursing. They can also move into education or pursue their doctorate for even higher salaries.

6. Become a Leader

MSN holders have the advanced clinical skills and management strategy knowledge to supervise employees and run nursing teams and departments.

7. Become a Nurse Anesthetist

Certified registered nurse anesthetists earn around $150,000 per year, and chief nurse anesthetists take home close to $180,000 annually.

8. Experience Greater Personal Fulfillment

Earning a master's degree has been shown to improve self-esteem and provide people with a real sense of accomplishment. All that new-found confidence may then lead to a better job and even a happier home life.

9. Experience a Longer, More Distinguished Career

By earning your MSN you will escape the long shifts, hours spent on the feet, and high stress that can accompany working as an RN. Instead, you will have less strenuous administrative duties, which will allow you to hold onto your job for much longer as you age.

10. Gain More Responsibility

Earning a master's degree could lead to you overseeing a department or facility. You could also be responsible for checking other nurses' work while also attending to your own patients.

Here are 15 Things You can do with an MSN Degree

- Pain management nurse
- HIV/AIDS nurse
- Nurse administrator
- Managed care nurse
- Nurse researcher
- Certified registered nurse assistant
- Nurse practitioner

- Nurse attorney
- Certified nurse midwife
- HIV/AIDS nurse
- Nurse administrator
- Psychiatric nurse practitioner
- Clinical nurse specialist
- Nurse researcher
- Occupational health nurse
- Gerontology nurse practitioner
- Hematology nurse
- Occupational health nurse
- Nurse attorney
- Legal nurse consultant

(Source: Monster)

Of course, earning a master's degree or a doctorate are not the only ways to boost your income. **There are other degrees and certificates that can raise your earnings significantly as well.**

Here are the most common career-boosting nursing degrees that are currently available, according to AllNursingSchools.com:

Bachelor of Science in Nursing

A Bachelor of Science in Nursing (BSN) is a 4-year degree designed for RNs who want to pursue supervisory roles and qualify for **higher-paying jobs**.

With a combination of academic classwork and on-site clinical training, you'll learn about scientific areas **such as** anatomy, **biology,** and **chemistry**, as well as specific duties related to patient care, laboratory testing, designing treatment plans, and assisting with surgery.

Some schools even offer programs that allow you to earn a BSN in a particular specialty of nursing such as acute care, geriatric nursing, infectious disease, pediatrics, and psychiatry, just to name a few. Specializing can often increase your job opportunities and potential earnings.

Who it's for

If you're ready to work as a RN, a BSN could be right for you if you have the time and financial resources to commit to 4 years. A BSN is also an ideal starting place if your ultimate goal is to earn a master's degree and work as an advanced practice nurse.

However, as the demand for nurses with BSNs grows, more schools are catering their programs to **students** beyond the categories listed above. Depending on your situation, you can find a traditional program or one designed to apply education you've already earned.

Traditional BSN

Traditional BSN degree programs are intended for recent high school graduates who have little to no professional healthcare experience. Requirements are similar to other bachelor's degree programs, though specific science prerequisites may be necessary.

LPN-to-BSN

LPN-to-BSN degree programs, often called "bridge programs," allow LPNs/LVNs to get degree credit for their previous education and experience. For these students, earning a BSN usually requires taking liberal arts coursework not offered in LPN/LVN programs.

RN-to-BSN

RN-to-BSN degree programs are designed for RNs who already have an associate's degree. Graduates of accredited ADN programs often transfer educational credits to meet some of the BSN course requirements, meaning they can earn their bachelor's in a less amount of time.

Second degree BSN

Second degree BSNs **are meant for career changers who hold a previous bachelor's degree in a non-nursing field.** These programs allow students to satisfy some of the BSN's liberal arts requirements by transferring credits from their first degree, again lessening the length of time.

Length of time

Traditional BSN programs require 4 years of full-time study. Students who have LPN or RN licensing, or bachelor's degree in a different field, might qualify for alternative BSN programs that could be completed in 1–2 years.

Since so many working RNs pursue BSNs for career advancement, there are many flexible part-time and online options, though they may extend your time to completion.

What you can do with this degree

If you don't already have your RN license from a previous associate's degree, earning a BSN will qualify you to sit for the required NCLEX-RN licensing exam. With job growth for RNs predicted to grow by 15% through 2026, you're likely to find a wide range of job opportunities with this degree.

More than half of RNs work in hospitals, though with your additional clinical experience and any specialized skills, you can find a variety of less traditional roles. These could include:

- Case manager
- Occupational health nurse
- Public health nurse
- School nurse
- Forensic nurse
- Legal nurse consultant
- Home health nurse
- Mid-level nurse administrator
- Home health nurse
- Case manager
- Parish nurse
- Legal nurse consultant
- Nursing informatics specialist
- Occupational health nurse
- Parish nurse
- Public health nurse
- School nurse

What you can earn

As with RNs with associate's degree, salaries vary based on a number of different factors. **While the average for all RNs is $75,510, those in the top 10% earn more than $106,000 per year.** With a BSN, you can often expect to make more than with an associate's.

Master of Science in Nursing

A Master of Science in Nursing (MSN) is a graduate program of study designed for nurses who want to practice in a specialized role known as an advanced practice registered nurse (APRN).

The curriculum is an MSN program is tailored far more than a general nursing degree. You'll dive deep into a concentrated area of study while taking advanced courses in topics such as leadership, management, healthcare policy, and research.

Who it's for

Requirements vary by program, but MSNs are typically designed for licensed RNs who have already completed a bachelor's-level education. That said, some MSN programs offer admission to RNs with associate's degrees, allowing them to pursue a bachelor's and master's simultaneously.

You might qualify for an MSN program if you're in one of the following groups:

- Students with accredited BSN degrees and current RN licenses

- RNs with extensive clinical experience but no BSN

- Career changers with bachelor's degrees in non-nursing but related fields

Length of time

Students who begin MSN programs with a BSN typically take about 2 years to complete their degree. If you're pursuing an MSN without BSN credentials or with a bachelor's in another field, you can expect roughly 3 years.

What you can do with this degree

With an MSN, you'll be prepared to work as an APRN in your area of concentration. To do so, you'll need you hold a state license as an RN as well as a national credential in your specialty. Specializations vary by program, but common options include the following:

Nurse practitioner

A **nurse practitioner's (NP)** duties are similar to those of physicians. While some states require NPs to work under a physician's supervision, NPs have more responsibility for diagnosing and treating **patients** than traditional RNs.

Clinical nurse specialist

Working as a clinical nurse specialist (CNS) involves applying advanced training and education to a specific patient group or type of treatment. The specialty area of a CNS can be defined by a specific population, disease, type of care, or treatment setting.

Certified nurse midwife

The role of a certified nurse midwife (CNM) includes working with mothers during pregnancy, birth, and postpartum phases. CNMs are considered primary providers in all 50 states.

Certified nurse anesthetist

A certified nurse anesthetist (CNA) works closely with physicians to safely administer anesthesia prior to procedures, monitor the patient during surgery, oversee the recovery, and develop plans for pain management. Due to the risk factors involved with anesthesia, some hospitals may require their anesthetists to have doctoral degrees.

What you can earn

The salaries of APRNs vary depending on the exact job title, where they work, and level of responsibility. As of

2018, the BLS offers these general guidelines for average salaries:

- **Nurse practitioners** and clinical **nurse specialists**: $110,030 per year

- **Nurse midwives**: $106,910

- **Nurse anesthetists**: $174,790

Joint Master's Degrees in Nursing

Earning a joint master's degree in nursing could be right for you if you want to earn an MSN and a complementary degree in less time than completing 2 separate programs. You'll get a solid education in nursing practice and theory while gaining advanced skills in another area that can help you tailor your career.

Who they're for

Joint master's degrees are designed for nurses who want to guide their careers toward specific types of leadership positions. Keep in mind that in order to pursue a joint degree you have to gain admission into each separate program. These degrees are meant for very serious students only, as you'll need to work on 2 demanding course loads at the same time.

Length of time

It typically takes between 18 months and 3 years of full-time study to complete a joint master's degree in nursing. While part-time and online options are available to accommodate working schedules, they'll likely extend your time to completion.

What you can do with these degrees

Any joint degree will expand your opportunities for advancement and higher earnings. Specific roles will depend on the type of degrees you earn, but there are 3 common combinations.

Joint MSN/MPH

Pairing an MSN with a Master of Public Health (MPH) is designed for nurses who want to pursue leadership positions in community or public health organizations.

Joint MSN/MBA

Combining an MSN with a Master of Business Administration (MBA) is sometimes known as being in the "Nurse Executive Program." Here, students learn the business skills necessary to hold executive-level roles in hospitals and other large healthcare organizations.

Joint MSN/MPH

Joint MSN/MHA

Earning an MSN with a Master of Health Administration (MHA) offers similar benefits to those of the joint degrees listed above, but the combination is a bit broader. You'll be educated about making important decisions related to the management of various healthcare organizations and educational settings.

What **you** can earn

The BLS doesn't report data for jobs that specifically require joint degrees, however, roles that fall under the general umbrella of healthcare executives and administrators earn an **average** annual wage of $113,730.

According to hundreds of salaries submitted to PayScale, chief nursing officers make an average of $126,318 a year. Those who go on to become vice presidents or CEOs of healthcare organizations or related nonprofits might see their salary climb even higher.

Doctoral Degrees in Nursing

Doctoral degrees in nursing are terminal degrees intended to help students gain the knowledge necessary to teach at the university level, conduct research in the field, or pursue high-level roles similar to those for students with joint master's degrees.

Who they're for

In some programs, these degrees are only for those who have their master's. In others, BSN graduates may qualify for programs that allow them to earn an MSN and doctoral **degree** at the same time. No matter what type of program you choose, you'll need to enter with a degree specifically in nursing and clinical experience under your belt.

Length of time

On average, a doctoral degree in nursing **takes** anywhere from **3–6 years to** complete, though your timeline depends on the type of degree you seek.

What you can do **with** this degree

Your **career** opportunities will vary, but there are 3 primary options based on your degree.

Doctor of Nursing Practice **(DNP)**

A DNP is a practice-oriented degree that emphasizes clinical leadership and advanced theory. It can help you qualify for higher-**paying executive positions** in **hospitals and** other **healthcare organizations.**

Doctor of Nursing Philosophy (PhD)

A nursing PhD focuses on scientific content and the creation of new research in the field. PhD programs **typically** include the completion of a dissertation and research papers. This degree can help you qualify for **leadership positions in research and academia.**

Doctor of Nursing Science (DNSc or DNS)

The Doctor of Nursing Science (DNSc or DNS) is a research-based doctoral degree. Like a PhD, it prepares graduates for roles as nurse educators and researchers.

What you can earn

As with those with a joint master's degree, it's hard to say exactly what you might earn with a doctorate in nursing. Salaries can vary by tens of thousands of dollars depending on your position, your employer, your location, and more. Nurse educators at the university level earn an average annual wage of $80,380, while executives in research facilities might make more than $150,000 a year.

(Source: Nursejournal.com)

Bonus Strategy

Get Creative With a Side Job

Summary:

In addition to the 6 techniques I've discussed in this book, another option to increasing your income would be to take up a "side hustle."

When looking for ways to make extra money, some nurses find that side jobs can be a great way to boost their income.

I, myself, am an example of this. In addition to being a nurse practitioner by day, I'm also a sports bar owner by night.

I'm the proud owner and operator of Diamonds Sports Bar & Grill in Calumet Park, IL, and RedKiva, which is located in Chicago's west loop area. I've also run two successful nightclubs in the Chicago-land area over the past 5 years.

Here are just a few side jobs that you could take advantage of to push your yearly earnings over six figures:

- Tutoring nursing students online

- Opening an Internet-based business – like writing or selling handmade crafts

- Teaching patients how to use medical equipment at home

- Providing care for homebound patients

- Working on weekends or vacation as a camp nurse

- Writing for nursing publications or nursing blogs

- Giving flu injections at special clinics

- Teaching patient education classes

The possibilities in this area are practically limitless. Just pursue something you enjoy and/or have an aptitude for. You don't want to be stuck doing something you don't like as this could spill over into other areas of your life and create more problems that what the extra cash is worth.

Conclusion

So there you have it – six ways to grow your salary and start making six figures a nurse ... along with a bonus strategy.

Let's quickly recap what we've discussed:

1. Pursue a specialty
Choose a specialty that interests you or that you have an aptitude for – and watch your salary grow.

2. Work 12 hour shifts

Doing this will allow you to more easily pick up an extra shift and receive higher overtime pay.

Do this consistently and your income will really take off.

3. Get certified

Research clearly shows that certified nurses have a better chance to earn top pay in their field.

4. Join a committee

Joining your organization's committee will give you valuable information and connections that you can leverage for higher pay in the future.

5. Become a Travel Nurse

Experienced nurses can earn excellent compensation as a travel nurse. Plus, the majority of your expenses will also be covered – allowing you to bank even more cash! If you are able to travel, there probably isn't a faster way to make six figures!

6. Earn a Higher Degree

Research by the American Association of Colleges of Nursing found that 79 percent of RN employers prefer to hire nurses with a bachelor's of science in nursing (BSN) degree as entry level employees. Meanwhile, earning a master's degree can open up a fast pathway to six figure earnings.

7. Bonus – Find a Side Job

If you can find a side job you enjoy it can be a great way to make money while also relieving the stress that can come with nursing.

Just Remember, Achieving Something BIG in Your Life Takes Massive ACTION!

So Are You Ready to CHANGE Your Earnings & Your Life?

For a variety of reasons – such as a lack of knowledge, fear of the unknown, etc. – many people go through life underachieving and never experiencing all that they could get out of life.

This is a shame. But it doesn't have to be that way for you. Not any longer. Put the techniques revealed in this book to work for you and you can rest assured that you will increase your income.

It's all about you taking action.

Don't be like so many people who get a book like this and learn what they are supposed to do and then never follow through.

If you are tired of "just getting by" ... if you really want to raise your income ... this book contains the steps you need to take.

Ask yourself where you want to be in six months or a year from now.

Do you still want to be lamenting your salary and wishing you were making more ... or do you want to have taken specific action that will either have you already earning more or well on your way to satisfying your goals?

You have the knowledge ... now the choice of what to do next is yours.

About the Author

Princess Lomax MSN, APRN, FNP-C, WCC

Princess Lomax is a Family Nurse Practitioner by day and a Sports Bar Owner by night.

She received her Bachelor of Science in Nursing from Benedictine University & a Master's of Science in Family Nurse Practitioner from Olivet Nazarene University.

She is currently enrolled at Valparaiso University as a Doctorial student.

As a Family Nurse Practitioner, Princess currently conducts in-home assessments for the Medicare population and provides primary care services for adults 65 years and older.

Princess has also been the proud owner and operator of Diamonds Sports Bar & Grill located in Calumet Park, IL, and RedKiva, located in Chicago's west loop area. She has also run two successful nightclubs in the Chicago-land area over the past 5 years.

In 2012, Princess founded the non-profit John Lomax Foundation, which provides underprivileged children with book bags & school supplies during her annual book bag giveaway in Chicago's Englewood Sherman Park area.

With her passion for giving back, Princess also feeds and clothes the homeless every year during the Thanksgiving & Christmas holiday seasons.

In 2018, she created another non-for-profit, which is called Red Door Development. This organization is responsible for teaching young adults on the job training skills that could potentially lead to permanent job placements.

Princess is a Partner of The Daughters of Englewood & We R' Englewood organizations that host charity events to provide assistance for the residents in the Englewood community.

Her latest passion is hosting a weekly Women Empowerment Series, where a group of 25 women study a workbook named "Empowered Women Win!"

Princess' focus is on bringing women together that can and will support, empower, commend, uplift, inspire, & pray for one another.

She is destined and determined to win in all aspects of life while inspiring others to do the same!

Here are a few quick tips to help you generate your next 6 figure income!

- Open an account with either a nursing credit union or a credit union connected to your employer and have $50-100 taken out of your check and deposited into that account.

- Don't activate the debit card so that you're unable to spend any money from that account. Before you know it, your savings in that account will start to grow.

- Instead of buying Starbucks every morning, invest in a coffee maker either for your house or the unit you work on and make your own coffee every morning. That small step could allow you to save $25-50 per week,

- Do weekly food preps and make your lunch instead of ordering out every day, which could save you $50-100 a week.

- Carpool with a couple of coworkers and save money utilized for gas.

- Start investing your annual savings into something you love or you're passionate about which can turn into a small business that will generate another income

Made in the USA
San Bernardino, CA
17 January 2020

63301811R00068